To My Boyfriend, I Want to Hear Your Story

THE GUIDED JOURNAL AND ACTIVITY BOOK FOR HIM TO SHARE HIS STORY WITH YOU

JEFFREY MASON

HEAR YOUR STORY BOOKS

HEAR YOUR STORY

ISBN: 978-1-955034-48-7

TABLE OF CONTENTS

This Person

_____

Gave This Person

_____

THIS BOOK BECAUSE THEY THINK (KNOW)
THEY ARE AWESOME AND WANT
TO LEARN MORE ABOUT THEM
AND THEIR LIFE STORY.

Using This Book

WOW! LOOK AT **YOU**!

YOU SHOULD TILT THAT CHIN UP JUST SLIGHTLY, PUT THOSE SHOULDERS BACK, AND WALK AROUND THE SCHOOL GYMNASIUM LIKE YOU JUST CRANE KICKED AN ENTIRE DOJO.

WHY?

WELL FOR STARTERS, YOU'RE **YOU** WHICH MEANS YOU ARE PACKED WITH ALL KINDS OF SEVERE SPECIALNESS. THERE HAS NEVER BEEN ANYONE LIKE YOU AND THERE WILL NEVER BE ANYONE LIKE YOU AGAIN (WE'RE SAYING THAT IN A NICE WAY.)

ANOTHER REASON? WELL, IF YOU HAVE THIS BOOK, IT IS BECAUSE YOU HAVE A **SOMEONE SPECIAL** YOU ARE GIVING IT TO...

OR...

SOMEONE SPECIAL GAVE IT TO **YOU** BECAUSE THEY WANT TO LEARN A WHOLE BUNCH MORE ABOUT **YOU**.

IF YOU ASK US, BOTH ARE PRETTY GREAT.

WE TOLD **YOU** THAT YOU ARE DANG EXCEPTIONAL AND EXTRAORDINARY.

SO, WHAT'S THE DEAL WITH THIS BOOK?

THE DEAL IS THAT THIS BOOK WAS MADE SO YOU COULD HAVE ALL KINDS OF **FUN** SHARING THE TALE AND TALES OF **YOU**.

EACH PAGE IS PLUM FULL OF QUESTIONS AND ACTIVITIES, EXPERTLY DESIGNED TO GUIDE **YOU** IN SHARING A LITTLE (OR MORE) OF **YOUR** LIFE STORY.

THERE ARE QUESTIONS ABOUT YOUR CHILDHOOD AND TEENS AND FAMILY AND DREAMS AND GOALS. THERE ARE OTHERS THAT GIVE YOU ROOM TO SAY, "HERE IS WHAT I THINK."

THERE ARE ALSO A FEW (JUST A FEW) THAT ARE A LITTLE DEEP AND REQUIRE A BIT OF VULNERABILITY (BUT IN A GOOD WAY).

THAT SAID, **YOU** GET TO DECIDE HOW MUCH **YOU** WANT TO SHARE.

LASTLY, THERE ARE OPPORTUNITIES TO TALK ABOUT THAT **SOMEONE SPECIAL**. THIS BOOK GIVES YOU ROOM TO SHARE WHAT YOU THINK ABOUT THEM, YOUR MEMORIES, AND EVEN WHAT YOUR BEST GUESS IS ON WHAT **THEY** WOULD SAY.

SO, GET OUT A PENCIL OR A PEN AND A BEVERAGE OF YOUR CHOICE, AND LET YOURSELF SHARE A BUNCH ABOUT **YOU**.

THEN PASS IT BACK TO THE PERSON WHO GAVE IT TO **YOU** AND SEE WHAT WOWS THEM. AND THEN TALK. TALKING IS GREAT!

AND HAVE **FUN**. DEFINITELY THAT!

"The best way for you to know me and me to know you is for us to hear each other's stories."
– Author Unknown

Once Upon a Time
(THAT MEANS "IN THE PAST" IN PRINCE CHARMING LANGUAGE)

SHARE A LITTLE ABOUT THE DAY YOU WERE BORN:

THIS IS THE DAY I WAS BORN...

_____

I WAS BORN IN THIS TOWN...

_____

AND THE PLACE I WAS BORN WAS (HOSPITAL, AT HOME, SIDE OF THE ROAD, ETC.) ...

_____

_____

MY FULL NAME AT BIRTH WAS...

_____

_____

THIS NAME WAS SELECTED FOR ME BECAUSE...

_____

_____

_____

_____

IF THEY HAD GIVEN ME A VOTE, I WOULD HAVE ASKED TO BE NAMED...

_____

_____

THIS IS HOW MUCH I WEIGHED WHEN I WAS BORN...

_____

AND I WAS THIS LONG...

_____

WHEN I WAS BORN, MY PARENT'S AGES WERE...

_____

_____

MY FIRST WORDS WERE...

_____

_____

_____

AND I TOOK MY FIRST STEPS AT THIS AGE...

_____

_____

(If you were adopted...)

I WAS THIS AGE WHEN MY PARENTS ADOPTED ME...

_____

AND I WAS THIS AGE WHEN I FOUND OUT I HAD BEEN ADOPTED...

_____

I WAS TOLD BY...

_____

I WOULD DESCRIBE MYSELF WHEN I WAS A KID THIS WAY...

_____

_____

_____

_____

THIS IS WHAT I KNOW ABOUT MY BIRTH PARENTS...

_____

_____

_____

_____

WHEN MY PARENTS AND OTHERS TALK ABOUT HOW I WAS AS A BABY, THEY DESCRIBE ME THIS WAY (ANSWER WITH A DESCRIPTION, POEM, OR DRAWING.) ...

"I'm looking into your eyes because I want to see what you see."
- Abigail Jeffries

I was this age when I learned to...

- SAY MY A, B, C'S: _____
- READ: _____
- WRITE MY NAME: _____
- WRITE MY NAME IN CURSIVE: _____
- GET DRESSED BY MYSELF: _____
- TIE MY SHOES: _____
- TIE A TIE: _____
- SHAVE: _____
- DO LAUNDRY: _____
- IRON: _____
- VACUUM: _____
- SEW ON A BUTTON: _____
- USE A SCREWDRIVER: _____
- USE A SAW: _____
- CHANGE A LIGHTBULB: _____
- UNCLOG A TOILET: _____
- PAINT A WALL: _____
- DO A CARTWHEEL: _____
- ROLLER SKATE: _____
- SKATEBOARD: _____

I was this age when I learned to...

- RIDE A BIKE (TWO-WHEEL): _____
- RIDE A HORSE: _____
- RIDE A MOTORCYCLE: _____
- DRIVE A CAR: _____
- PARALLEL PARK: _____
- DRIVE A STICK SHIFT CAR: _____
- CHANGE A TIRE: _____
- CHANGE THE OIL IN A CAR: _____
- SWIM: _____
- DIVE FROM A DIVING BOARD: _____
- WATER SKI: _____
- SURF: _____
- SCUBA DIVE: _____
- RIDE A SLED: _____
- SNOW SKI: _____
- SNOW BOARD: _____
- CATCH A BALL: _____
- THROW A BALL: _____
- SLOW DANCE: _____
- FAST DANCE: _____

I was this age when I learned to...

- WHISTLE: _____

- PLAY A MUSICAL INSTRUMENT: _____

- SHAKE HANDS: _____

- PROPERLY KISS: _____

- PLAY SPIN THE BOTTLE: _____

- APPRECIATE WHAT "THE BIRDS AND THE BEES" REALLY MEANS: _____

- MAKE A CUP OF COFFEE: _____

- OPEN A BOTTLE OF WINE (CORKED): _____

- MAKE A COCKTAIL: _____

- GROCERY SHOP: _____

- COOK A MEAL FOR A GROUP OF PEOPLE: _____

- SET THE TABLE: _____

- DO DISHES: _____

- DO ADDITION AND SUBTRACTION: _____

- DO MULTIPLICATION AND DIVISION: _____

- TELL TIME: _____

- WRITE A CHECK: _____

- DO MY TAXES: _____

- MAKE A RESUME: _____

I was this age when I learned to...

- INTERVIEW FOR A JOB: _____
- VOTE: _____
- MAKE MY OWN DOCTOR/DENTIST APPOINTMENT: _____
- READ A MAP: _____
- HOLD A BABY: _____
- CHANGE A DIAPER: _____
- CALM A CRYING BABY: _____
- FEED A BABY: _____
- SHUFFLE CARDS: _____
- DO A CARD TRICK: _____
- PLAY POKER: _____
- PLAY BLACKJACK: _____
- PLAY POOL: _____
- FISH: _____
- SHOOT A GUN: _____
- CHOP WOOD: _____
- SET UP A TENT: _____
- START A CAMPFIRE: _____
- THROW A PUNCH: _____
- BLOCK A PUNCH: _____

Let's chat about childhood...

WHEN I WAS A KID, MOST PEOPLE CALLED ME...

_____

BUT SOMETIMES THEY WOULD USE THIS NICKNAME...

_____

I WAS GIVEN THIS NICKNAME BECAUSE...

_____

_____

I WOULD DESCRIBE MYSELF WHEN I WAS A KID THIS WAY...

_____

_____

_____

_____

...AND MY CHILDHOOD THIS WAY...

_____

_____

_____

_____

DURING MY ELEMENTARY SCHOOL YEARS, MY BEST FRIENDS
WERE...

_____

_____

_____

_____

THE LAST TIME I SPOKE WITH ANY OF THEM WAS...

_____

_____

_____

THE ELEMENTARY SCHOOL TEACHER THAT I MOST FONDLY
REMEMBER IS...

_____

THE THING I MOST REMEMBER ABOUT THIS TEACHER IS...

_____

_____

_____

WHEN I WAS A KID, MY REGULAR CHORES INCLUDED...

_____

_____

_____

_____

IN RETURN, I RECEIVED AN ALLOWANCE OF...

_____

_____

WHEN I HAD MONEY, I WOULD TYPICALLY SPEND IT ON...

_____

_____

_____

WHEN I WAS A KID, I DREAMED OF BECOMING A...

_____

_____

_____

_____

ONE OF MY MOST FAVORITE CHILDHOOD MEMORIES IS...

_____

_____

_____

_____

_____

_____

_____

_____

_____

_____

_____

_____

_____

DURING MY CHILDHOOD, I SPENT MOST OF MY SUMMERS DOING THIS...

_____

_____

_____

_____

THIS IS WHERE WE LIVED DURING MY ELEMENTARY AND JUNIOR HIGH SCHOOL YEARS...

_____

_____

_____

THIS IS HOW I WOULD DESCRIBE WHERE WE LIVED...

_____

_____

_____

_____

_____

IF I COULD BE A KID AGAIN FOR JUST ONE DAY, I WOULD DO THE FOLLOWING (ANSWER WITH A DESCRIPTION, POEM, OR DRAWING.) ...

When I was a kid, I ...

- ☐ HAD AN IMAGINARY FRIEND.
- ☐ SHARED A BEDROOM.
- ☐ HAD TO SLEEP WITH A SPECIFIC TOY OR BLANKET.
- ☐ HAD A NIGHT LIGHT.
- ☐ LIKED TO BE TUCKED IN.
- ☐ WAS READ BEDTIME STORIES.
- ☐ WALKED TO SCHOOL.
- ☐ RODE MY BIKE TO SCHOOL.
- ☐ GOT A DETENTION.
- ☐ WAS SENT TO THE PRINCIPAL'S OFFICE.
- ☐ WAS IN A SCHOOL PLAY.
- ☐ HAD A CRUSH ON A CLASSMATE.
- ☐ HAD A CRUSH ON SOMEONE FAMOUS.
- ☐ WAS IN A SCHOOL SPELLING BEE.
- ☐ CAMPED IN THE BACKYARD.
- ☐ MADE FORTS.
- ☐ HAD A TREEHOUSE.
- ☐ CAUGHT FIREFLIES.
- ☐ HAD A TELESCOPE.
- ☐ WENT TO SUMMER CAMP.
- ☐ COLLECTED SHELLS ON THE BEACH.
- ☐ MADE A SANDCASTLE.

When I was a kid, I ...

☐ HAD A REPTILE, INSECT, OR ARACHNID FOR A PET.

☐ WAS IN A SNOWBALL FIGHT.

☐ MADE A SNOWMAN.

☐ HAD A LEMONADE STAND.

☐ HAD A PAPER ROUTE.

☐ TOOK MUSIC LESSONS.

☐ FLEW A KITE.

☐ ROLLER-SKATED.

☐ RODE A SKATEBOARD.

☐ READ COMIC BOOKS.

☐ COLLECTED SPORTS CARDS.

☐ PLAYED SPORTS.

☐ TOOK MARTIAL ARTS.

☐ GOT MONEY FROM THE TOOTH FAIRY.

☐ GOT ICE CREAM FROM AN ICE CREAM TRUCK.

☐ HAD SLEEPOVERS.

☐ SNUCK OUT OF THE HOUSE AT NIGHT.

☐ WROTE ON THE WALLS.

☐ WENT TO THE ZOO.

☐ WENT TO AN AMUSEMENT PARK.

☐ BROKE A BONE.

☐ HAD TO GET STICHES.

When I was a kid, I ...

I REMEMBER PLAYING THESE GAMES...

_____

_____

_____

_____

AND WITH THESE TOYS...

_____

_____

_____

_____

AND LOVING THESE TELEVISION SHOWS...

_____

_____

_____

_____

When I was a kid, I ...

AND THESE MOVIES...

_____

_____

_____

_____

AND THESE SONGS...

_____

_____

_____

_____

AND THESE BOOKS...

_____

_____

_____

_____

A few of my firsts...

MY FIRST PET WAS A...

_____

ITS NAME WAS...

_____

I GOT MY FIRST CAR WHEN I WAS THIS AGE...

_____

MY FIRST CAR I OWNED ON MY OWN WAS A (YEAR, MAKE, AND MODEL) ...

_____

I GOT MY TRAFFIC TICKET WHEN I WAS THIS AGE...

_____

I RECEIVED THIS TICKET BECAUSE...

_____

_____

_____

AND THIS IS WHAT I HAD TO DO AND PAY...

_____

_____

_____

THE FIRST ALBUM/TAPE/CD I CAN REMEMBER BUYING WAS...

_____

_____

THE FIRST MUSIC CONCERT I ATTENDED WAS...

_____

_____

MY FIRST IMPRESSIONS OF MY GIRLFRIEND WERE...

_____

_____

_____

_____

_____

_____

_____

_____

_____

"Assumptions are the termites of relationships."

– Henry Winkler

My teen years...

I WOULD DESCRIBE MYSELF WHEN I WAS A TEENAGER THIS WAY...

_____

_____

_____

_____

_____

_____

_____

_____

_____

_____

_____

THIS IS HOW I DRESSED AND STYLED MY HAIR DURING MY HIGH
SCHOOL YEARS...

PASTE A PICTURE OF YOU FROM YOUR HIGH SCHOOL YEARS.

DURING MY TEENAGE YEARS, THE PEOPLE I MAINLY HUNG OUT
WITH WERE...

_____

_____

_____

_____

_____

THE LAST TIME WE TALKED WAS...

_____

_____

_____

MY PARENTS' OPINION OF MY CHOICE IN FRIENDS WAS...

_____

_____

_____

_____

A TYPICAL WEEKEND NIGHT DURING MY HIGH SCHOOL YEARS
WAS SPENT...

_____

_____

_____

_____

MY CURFEW IN HIGH SCHOOL WAS...

_____

_____

ONE MEMORABLE TIME I MISSED MY CURFEW WAS BECAUSE...

_____

_____

_____

_____

_____

MY PARENTS' REACTION TO MY MISSING CURFEW WAS...

_____

_____

_____

_____

THE THREE WORDS I WOULD USE TO DESCRIBE MY HIGH SCHOOL
DATING LIFE ARE...

_____

_____

_____

I GOT MY DRIVER'S LICENSE WHEN I WAS THIS AGE...

_____

TO GET MY LICENSE, I HAD TO TAKE MY DRIVING TEST THIS MANY
TIMES...

_____

THE PERSON WHO TAUGHT ME TO DRIVE WAS...

_____

_____

THE YEAR, MAKE, AND MODEL OF THE CAR I LEARNED HOW TO DRIVE IN WAS...

_____

_____

THE YEAR I GRADUATED I FROM HIGH SCHOOL WAS...

_____

MY GRADUATING CLASS HAD THIS MANY STUDENTS IN IT...

_____

MY GRADES WERE TYPICALLY IN THIS RANGE...

_____

_____

_____

MY FAVORITE AND LEAST FAVORITE SUBJECTS WERE...

_____

_____

_____

_____

_____

THE THINGS I LIKED THE MOST ABOUT HIGH SCHOOL WERE...

_____

_____

_____

_____

_____

_____

_____

...AND THESE ARE THE THINGS I COULD HAVE DONE WITHOUT...

_____

_____

_____

_____

_____

_____

_____

THE SCHOOL ACTIVITIES AND SPORTS THAT I PARTICIPATED IN
WERE...

_____

_____

_____

_____

_____

_____

WHEN I WAS A TEENAGER, I SPENT MY SUMMERS...

_____

_____

_____

_____

_____

_____

KNOWING WHAT I KNOW NOW, THE ADVICE I WOULD GIVE MY
TEENAGE SELF IS...

_____

_____

_____

_____

_____

_____

_____

_____

_____

_____

_____

A TEACHER, COACH, OR MENTOR THAT HAD A HUGE IMPACT ON ME BECOMING WHO I AM TODAY IS...

_____

_____

_____

THE SPECIFIC INFLUENCES THEY HAD ON ME, AND MY LIFE WERE...

_____

_____

_____

_____

_____

_____

_____

_____

MY BEDROOM FROM MY TEENAGE YEARS LOOKED LIKE THIS...

IF I HAD TO DESCRIBE IT, I WOULD SAY THE OVERALL THEME
WAS...

_____

_____

_____

THE WALLS WERE THIS COLOR...

_____

_____

MY BEDDING LOOKED LIKE THIS...

_____

_____

I HAD THESE THINGS ON THE WALLS...

_____

_____

_____

_____

_____

AND MY FAVORITE PLACE TO HIDE THINGS WAS...

_____

_____

_____

ADDITIONAL IMPORTANT DETAILS INCLUDE...

_____

_____

_____

_____

_____

_____

_____

_____

_____

When I was a teenager, I...

LOVED THESE BANDS/MUSICIANS...

_____

_____

_____

_____

_____

AND THESE BOOKS...

_____

_____

_____

_____

_____

When I was a teenager...

AND THESE MOVIES...

_____

_____

_____

_____

_____

_____

AND THESE TELEVISION SHOWS...

_____

_____

_____

_____

_____

_____

My all-time Top 30 favorite songs ever playlist:

1. _____

2. _____

3. _____

4. _____

5. _____

6. _____

7. _____

8. _____

9. _____

10. _____

11. _____

12. _____

13. _____

14. _____

15. _____

16. _____

17. _____

18. _____

19. _____

20. _____

21. _____

22. _____

23. _____

24. _____

25. _____

26. _____

27. _____

28. _____

29. _____

30. _____

"Don't try to be something to everyone. Be everything to someone."
– Author Unknown

Adult time...

AFTER HIGH SCHOOL I MADE THE CHOICE TO...

- ☐ START COLLEGE.
- ☐ JOIN THE MILITARY.
- ☐ GET A JOB.
- ☐ TAKE A BREAK.
- ☐ OTHER: _____

I MADE THIS DECISION BECAUSE...

_____

_____

_____

_____

_____

_____

LOOKING BACK, THIS IS HOW I NOW FEEL ABOUT MY DECISION...

- ☐ IT WAS THE RIGHT ONE, AT THE RIGHT TIME.
- ☐ IT WAS THE RIGHT DIRECTION TO GO IN, BUT THE WRONG TIME TO DO IT.
- ☐ YOU CAN'T GET THEM ALL RIGHT.
- ☐ THE JURY'S STILL OUT.

I THINK THAT THIS WAS THE CORRECT OR INCORRECT DECISION
BECAUSE...

_____

_____

_____

_____

_____

_____

THIS IS HOW THIS PERIOD IMPACTED MY LIFE...

_____

_____

_____

_____

_____

_____

IF I HAD A REDO, I WOULD MAKE THESE CHANGES TO THIS PERIOD
OF MY LIFE...

_____

_____

_____

_____

_____

_____

I GOT MY FIRST JOB WHEN I WAS THIS AGE...

_____

THE JOB WAS...

_____

_____

...AND I WAS PAID THIS MUCH...

_____

My first house/apartment in six questions...

THE FIRST PLACE I LIVED ON MY OWN OR WITH ROOMMATES
WAS...

_____

_____

I MOVED HERE WHEN I WAS THIS AGE...

_____

IT HAD THIS MANY BEDROOMS AND BATHROOMS...

_____

_____

I LIVED THERE WITH...

_____

_____

_____

MY SHARE OF THE RENT/MORTGAGE WAS...

_____

_____

My first apartment in six questions...

THIS IS HOW I WOULD DESCRIBE THIS PLACE...

_____

_____

_____

_____

_____

_____

_____

_____

_____

_____

_____

_____

Pick One...

CARD GAMES	OR	BOARD GAMES
STREAMING	OR	VINYL
NICE HOUSE	OR	NICE CAR
BEACH	OR	WOODS
SETTLE DOWN SOON	OR	SETTLE DOWN EVENTUALLY
BEER OR WINE	OR	COCKTAILS
CALL	OR	TEXT
CHANGE THE PAST	OR	SEE THE FUTURE
BOOK VERSION	OR	MOVIE VERSION
WEEKLY RELIGIOUS SERVICES	OR	I HAVE MY OWN BELIEFS
LIVE IN TOWN	OR	LIVE ON LOTS OF LAND
TENT	OR	CABIN
PANCAKES	OR	WAFFLES
WORK OVERTIME	OR	FREE TIME
CHURCH WEDDING	OR	OUTDOOR WEDDING
I PREFER TO DRIVE	OR	I'M GOOD IF SHE DRIVES
PLAY VIDEO GAMES	OR	WATCH TELEVISION
LIGHT PACKER	OR	HEAVY PACKER
RELAXING VACATION	OR	EXPLORING VACATION

Pick One...

CARDIO	OR	LIFTING WEIGHTS
MOVIE AT THE THEATER	OR	MOVIE AT HOME
BOOK	OR	EBOOK
I STRICTLY FOLLOW A BUDGET	OR	I KNOW WHAT I CAN SPEND
HAVE KIDS ONE DAY	OR	NOT SURE/NOT FOR ME
SALTY	OR	SWEET
CAR	OR	TRUCK
SPEND	OR	SAVE/INVEST
COOK AT HOME	OR	ORDER IN/EAT OUT
DOUBLE INCOME	OR	STAY-AT-HOME PARENT
SMALL TOWN	OR	BIG CITY
WEEKENDS HOME	OR	WEEKENDS OUT
THINK FIRST	OR	LEAP FIRST
OPEN-MINDED	OR	KNOW WHAT I BELIEVE
ME: A LITTLE DEBT	OR	ME: A LOT OF DEBT
MAKE IT WORK	OR	TRY SOMETHING ELSE
OUTSIDE	OR	INDOORS
EXERCISE OFTEN	OR	EXERCISE SOMETIMES
WANT PETS	OR	NO PETS

My family...

THE THREE WORDS I WOULD USE TO DESCRIBE MY FAMILY ARE...

1. _____

2. _____

3. _____

THE TELEVISION FAMILY THAT REMINDS ME THE MOST OF MY FAMILY WHEN I WAS GROWING UP IS...

_____

_____

I HAVE THIS MANY BROTHERS AND SISTERS...

_____

I WAS THE OLDEST/MIDDLE/YOUNGEST OR ONLY CHILD...

_____

IN ORDER OF THEIR BIRTH, MY SIBLINGS' NAMES ARE...

_____

_____

_____

_____

My family...

A REALLY COOL FUN FACT ABOUT MY FAMILY IS...

_____

_____

_____

_____

_____

THE HOLIDAY THAT WAS THE BIGGEST DEAL IN OUR FAMILY
WAS...

_____

_____

A FEW OF THE WAYS WE CELEBRATED THIS HOLIDAY INCLUDED...

_____

_____

_____

_____

_____

My mom...

MY MOTHER'S FULL NAME IS...

_____

THE WAY I WOULD DESCRIBE HER IS...

_____

_____

_____

_____

_____

_____

_____

THIS IS WHERE SHE WAS BORN AND GREW UP...

_____

_____

_____

A REALLY COOL FUN FACT ABOUT MY MOTHER IS...

_____

_____

_____

_____

HER HIGHEST LEVEL OF EDUCATION AND OCCUPATIONS ARE...

_____

_____

_____

SHE AND I ARE ALIKE IN THESE WAYS...

_____

_____

_____

_____

_____

_____

ONE OF MY FAVORITE MEMORIES OF MY MOTHER IS...

_____

_____

_____

_____

_____

_____

SOME OF THE BEST ADVICE SHE EVER GAVE ME WAS...

_____

_____

_____

_____

_____

_____

My dad...

MY FATHER'S FULL NAME IS...

_____

THE WAY I WOULD DESCRIBE HIM IS...

_____

_____

_____

_____

_____

_____

_____

_____

THIS IS WHERE HE WAS BORN AND GREW UP...

_____

_____

_____

A REALLY COOL FUN FACT ABOUT MY FATHER IS...

_____

_____

_____

_____

HIS HIGHEST LEVEL OF EDUCATION AND OCCUPATIONS IS...

_____

_____

_____

HE AND I ARE ALIKE IN THESE WAYS...

_____

_____

_____

_____

_____

ONE OF MY FAVORITE MEMORIES OF MY FATHER IS...

_____

_____

_____

_____

_____

_____

SOME OF THE BEST ADVICE HE EVER GAVE ME WAS...

_____

_____

_____

_____

_____

MY PARENTS WERE MARRIED WHEN THEY WERE THIS AGE...

_____

_____

THEY HAVE BEEN/WERE MARRIED FOR THIS MANY YEARS...

_____

I WOULD DESCRIBE THEIR RELATIONSHIP THIS WAY...

_____

_____

_____

_____

THEIR RELATIONSHIP INFLUENCED HOW I FEEL ABOUT LOVE,
RELATIONSHIPS, AND MARRIAGE IN THE FOLLOWING WAYS...

_____

_____

_____

_____

I WOULD DESCRIBE MY RELATIONSHIP WITH MY PARENTS WHEN I WAS A KID THIS WAY...

_____

_____

_____

_____

...AND THIS WAY DURING MY TEENS...

_____

_____

_____

_____

...AND NOW...

_____

_____

_____

_____

My grandparents...

MY GRANDPARENTS' NAMES ON MY MOTHER'S SIDE ARE...

_____

MY GRANDPARENTS' NAMES ON MY FATHER'S SIDE ARE...

_____

THIS IS WHAT I CALLED THEM...

_____

_____

THIS IS HOW I WOULD DESCRIBE MY MOTHER'S PARENTS...

_____

_____

_____

THIS IS HOW I WOULD DESCRIBE MY FATHER'S PARENTS...

_____

_____

_____

A LIST OF PEOPLE OTHER THAN MY PARENTS WHO HELPED RAISE ME INCLUDES...

1. _____

2. _____

3. _____

4. _____

5. _____

6. _____

7. _____

8. _____

9. _____

10. _____

11. _____

12. _____

13. _____

14. _____

15. _____

The Story of How We Met...

USE THESE TWO PAGES TO TELL THE STORY OF HOW AND YOU YOUR GIRLFRIEND MET AS THOUGH IT WAS A FAIRY TALE.

FEEL FREE TO INCLUDE DRAGONS TO BE SLAIN, FROGS TO BE KISSED, SPELLS TO BE BROKEN, KNIGHTS IN SHINING ARMOR, AND PRINCESSES IN DISTRESS.

Once upon a time ago, in a land far, far away

Thoughts on love and romance and relationships...

IN MY OPINION, THE FIVE MOST IMPORTANT FACTORS IN KEEPING A RELATIONSHIP STRONG AND HEALTHY ARE...

1. _____

2. _____

3. _____

4. _____

5. _____

THE COUPLE I THINK IS A MODEL FOR A GREAT RELATIONSHIP IS...

_____

_____

THE QUALITIES I MOST ADMIRE ABOUT THEIR RELATIONSHIP ARE...

_____

_____

_____

_____

_____

I CAN TELL I AM DEVELOPING FEELINGS FOR SOMEONE WHEN I
START TO...

_____

_____

_____

_____

MY TOP THREE RELATIONSHIP DEAL BREAKERS ARE...

1. _____

2. _____

3. _____

IF I WERE PLANNING MY VERSION OF THE PERFECT DATE NIGHT, IT
WOULD INCLUDE ALL THE FOLLOWING...

_____

_____

_____

_____

_____

THE DESTINATION I WOULD PICK AS THE PERFECT ROMANTIC VACATION IS...

_____

_____

_____

MY FAVORITE ROMANTIC MOVIE IS...

_____

_____

AND THIS IS MY FAVORITE ROMANTIC SONG...

_____

_____

I WAS THIS AGE WHEN...

I HAD MY FIRST CRUSH: _____

I WENT ON MY FIRST DATE: _____

I HAD MY FIRST KISS: _____

I WAS IN MY FIRST STEADY RELATIONSHIP: _____

MY HEART WAS BROKEN THE FIRST TIME: _____

MET MY GIRLFRIEND: _____

ACCORDING TO THE BOOK, "THE 5 LOVE LANGUAGES," EACH OF US HAS A SPECIFIC WAY WE EXPRESS AND FEEL LOVE. THE FIVE WAYS ARE: WITH WORDS THAT SHOW AFFECTION, PRAISE AND APPRECIATION; SPENDING FOCUSED TIME TOGETHER; PHYSICAL AND AFFECTIONATE TOUCH; DOING NICE THINGS FOR EACH OTHER; GIVING AND RECEIVING GIFTS.

AFTER REVIEWING THIS LIST, I THINK MY PERSONAL LOVE LANGUAGE IS:

_____

_____

AND I THINK MY GIRLFRIEND'S IS:

_____

_____

BASED UPON WHAT I THINK HER LOVE LANGUAGE IS, THE THINGS I SHOULD MAKE SURE I DO MORE OFTEN ARE...

_____

_____

_____

_____

_____

I believe...

- ☐ IN SOUL MATES.

- ☐ IN LOVE AT FIRST SIGHT.

- ☐ THAT LOVE CAN LAST FOREVER.

- ☐ IT IS OKAY TO KISS ON THE FIRST DATE.

- ☐ IN LONG-DISTANCE RELATIONSHIPS.

- ☐ IN MARRIAGE.

- ☐ IN DIVORCE.

- ☐ THAT YOU CAN BE FRIENDS WITH AN EX.

- ☐ IT IS IMPORTANT TO CELEBRATE VALENTINE'S DAY.

- ☐ IN WILD ROMANTIC GESTURES.

- ☐ THAT YOU CAN FIND LOVE THROUGH ONLINE DATING.

- ☐ IT IS OKAY TO LIVE TOGETHER WITHOUT BEING MARRIED.

- ☐ IN SECOND CHANCES.

- ☐ IN THIRD CHANCES.

- ☐ THAT PEOPLE TEND TO HAVE A SPECIFIC TYPE THEY ARE ATTRACTED TO.

- ☐ MORE GUYS SHOULD LIKE ROMANTIC COMEDIES.

- ☐ THAT IT IS OKAY TO MOVE TO BE WITH SOMEONE.

- ☐ COUPLES SHOULD KNOW ABOUT EACH OTHER'S PAST RELATIONSHIPS.

- ☐ IT IS OKAY TO HAVE A RELATIONSHIP WITH SOMEONE YOU CLOSELY WORK WITH.

- ☐ TRUST CAN BE RESTORED.

I believe...

- ☐ IT IS IMPORTANT THAT A COUPLE GETS ALONG WITH EACH OTHER'S FRIENDS.

- ☐ IN THE OLD SAYING THAT WOMEN TEND TO DATE PEOPLE LIKE THEIR FATHER AND MEN PEOPLE LIKE THEIR MOTHER.

- ☐ THAT TEXTS AND CALLS SHOULD BE RESPONDED TO AS SOON AS POSSIBLE.

- ☐ IT IS IMPORTANT THAT A COUPLE CHECK IN WITH EACH OTHER ON A REGULAR BASIS.

- ☐ THAT COMPLETE HONESTY IS THE BEST POLICY.

- ☐ IN LOVE POEMS.

- ☐ IN LOVE SONGS.

- ☐ THAT A COUPLE SHOULD KNOW THE DETAILS OF EACH OTHER'S FINANCES.

- ☐ THAT IT IS OK TO HAVE SEPARATE VACATIONS.

- ☐ THAT LOVE IS BLIND.

- ☐ IT IS OKAY TO DATE SOMEONE WHO USED TO DATE A CLOSE FRIEND.

- ☐ THAT ONE OF THE MAIN POINTS TO GETTING MARRIED IS TO HAVE CHILDREN TOGETHER.

- ☐ YOUR PARTNER'S NEEDS COME FIRST.

- ☐ IT IS CRITICAL THAT BOTH PEOPLE IN A RELATIONSHIP HAVE THE SAME RELIGIOUS AND SPIRITUAL BELIEFS.

- ☐ IT IS OKAY TO NEED SOME ALONE TIME.

- ☐ THAT IT IS HEALTHY FOR INDIVIDUALS IN A RELATIONSHIP TO GROW AND CHANGE.

My girlfriend in 26 letters...

WRITE A WORD (OR MORE IF YOU WANT) THAT DESCRIBES YOUR GIRLFRIEND THAT BEGINS WITH EACH LETTER:

A:

B:

C:

D:

E:

F:

G:

H:

I:

J:

K:

L:

My girlfriend in 26 letters...

M:

N:

P:

Q:

R:

S:

T:

U:

V:

W:

X:

Y:

Z:

Some stuff about me...

IF I WERE TO WRITE AN AUTOBIOGRAPHY, THE TITLE WOULD BE...

_____

_____

_____

ONE OF MY FAVORITE QUOTES IS...

_____

_____

_____

_____

MY PERSONAL HERO IS...

_____

_____

_____

AND MY PERSONAL VILLAIN IS...

_____

_____

_____

THE SMARTEST THING I HAVE EVER DONE IS...

_____

_____

_____

_____

_____

_____

AND THE DUMBEST THING IS...

_____

_____

_____

_____

_____

THE BRAVEST THING I HAVE EVER DONE IS...

_____

_____

_____

_____

_____

ONE OF THE HARDEST DECISIONS OF MY LIFE WAS...

_____

_____

_____

_____

_____

THE HARDEST THING I HAVE HAD TO OVERCOME IN MY LIFE IS...

_____

_____

_____

_____

I SUCCEEDED IN OVERCOMING THIS CHALLENGE BECAUSE OF
THESE DECISIONS, ACTIONS, AND PEOPLE...

_____

_____

_____

_____

_____

_____

_____

I have...

- ☐ TRAVELED OVERSEAS.

- ☐ FLOWN IN A PLANE.

- ☐ HAD SURGERY.

- ☐ MILKED A COW.

- ☐ BEEN IN A FIST FIGHT.

- ☐ GONE ON A BLIND DATE.

- ☐ HAD MY TONSILS REMOVED.

- ☐ MADE A SPEECH IN FRONT OF A LARGE GROUP.

- ☐ SUNG A SOLO IN FRONT OF AN AUDIENCE.

- ☐ BEEN ARRESTED.

- ☐ RIDDEN A MOTORCYCLE.

- ☐ SHOT A GUN.

- ☐ RIDDEN IN A HOT AIR BALLOON.

- ☐ GONE ON A CRUISE.

- ☐ LIED TO A POLICE OFFICER.

- ☐ GONE SCUBA DIVING.

- ☐ HAD STICHES.

- ☐ RUN A MARATHON.

- ☐ AGREED TO BE SOMEONE ELSE'S ALIBI.

- ☐ GONE BUNGEE JUMPING.

I have...

☐ SKIPPED SCHOOL.

☐ LOST A SIGNIFICANT AMOUNT OF WEIGHT.

☐ RIDDEN IN A HELICOPTER.

☐ GOTTEN A TATTOO.

☐ BEEN TO A BROADWAY MUSICAL.

☐ USED A FAKE ID.

☐ BEEN TO A PROFESSIONAL SPORTING EVENT.

☐ MET A CELEBRITY.

☐ GONE SKYDIVING.

☐ BROKEN A BONE.

☐ CHEATED ON A TEST.

☐ BEEN TO A LARGE MUSIC FESTIVAL.

☐ SNOOPED THROUGH SOMEONE'S MEDICINE CABINET.

☐ GONE SURFING.

☐ PERFORMED IN A PLAY, MUSICAL, OR OPERA.

☐ LIED TO GET OUT OF WORK.

☐ GONE BACKPACKING.

☐ SNUCK INTO A MOVIE.

☐ BEEN TO THE GRAND CANYON.

☐ PARTICIPATED IN A POLITICAL PROTEST.

I have...

☐ STOOD UP A DATE.

☐ BEEN STOOD UP.

☐ GOTTEN A SPEEDING TICKET.

☐ GOTTEN OUT OF A SPEEDING TICKET.

☐ CRASHED A PARTY.

☐ HAD A CRUSH ON A CELEBRITY.

☐ HAD A CRUSH ON A TEACHER OR BOSS.

☐ BEEN SELECTED FOR A JURY.

☐ GIVEN SOMEONE A FAKE NAME OR PHONE NUMBER.

☐ BEEN IN A BAND.

☐ HAD A NEAR DEATH EXPERIENCE.

☐ PERFORMED CPR OR THE HEIMLICH MANEUVER ON SOMEONE.

☐ DRIVEN IN A COUNTRY WHERE THEY DRIVE ON THE OTHER SIDE OF THE ROAD.

☐ PLAYED SPIN THE BOTTLE.

☐ DRIVEN ON ROUTE 66.

☐ SEEN A METEOR SHOWER.

☐ CROWD-SURFED AT A MUSIC CONCERT.

☐ SLEPT OUTSIDE UNDER THE STARS.

☐ HAD MY APPENDIX REMOVED.

I have...

- ☐ LEARNED A SECOND LANGUAGE.

- ☐ BEEN STUCK IN AN ELEVATOR.

- ☐ HAD MY PALM READ.

- ☐ BROKEN OFF AN ENGAGEMENT.

- ☐ HAD BRACES.

- ☐ GONE ICE SKATING.

- ☐ GONE SNOW SKIING.

- ☐ GONE SLEDDING.

- ☐ BEEN TO A TROPICAL ISLAND.

- ☐ RIDDEN ON A TRAIN.

- ☐ GROWN A VEGETABLE GARDEN.

- ☐ STARTED A BUSINESS.

- ☐ EXPERIENCED AN EARTHQUAKE.

- ☐ BEEN IN A HURRICANE.

- ☐ BEEN WHERE A TORNADO STRUCK DOWN.

- ☐ DONATED BLOOD.

- ☐ MADE A SNOW ANGEL.

- ☐ LIVED IN A FOREIGN COUNTRY.

- ☐ BEEN TO A HOT SPRING.

- ☐ BEEN KNOCKED UNCONSCIOUS.

I have...

- ☐ GONE SAILING.
- ☐ BEEN TO A RODEO.
- ☐ GONE DEEP SEA FISHING.
- ☐ DRIVEN A TRACTOR.
- ☐ BEEN IN THE MIDDLE OF A MOSH PIT.
- ☐ BEEN CALLED UP ON STAGE AT A CONCERT/SHOW.
- ☐ BEEN TO A TOPLESS/NUDE BEACH.
- ☐ RIDDEN A MECHANICAL BULL.
- ☐ BEEN A PASSENGER IN A PRIVATE JET.
- ☐ DYED MY HAIR.
- ☐ HAD MY PICTURE TAKEN WITH SOMEONE FAMOUS.
- ☐ BEEN A MAID OF HONOR/BEST MAN.
- ☐ RE-GIFTED A GIFT.
- ☐ BEEN ON TELEVISION.
- ☐ SEEN A UFO.
- ☐ GONE SKINNY-DIPPING.
- ☐ ATTENDED THE BALLET.
- ☐ ADOPTED A PET.
- ☐ ATTENDED THE OPERA.
- ☐ RIDDEN IN A HORSE-DRAWN CARRIAGE.

"Nobody has ever measured,
not even poets, how much the
heart can hold."

– Zelda Fitzgerald

I am grateful for...

THESE EVERYDAY THINGS...

_____

_____

_____

_____

_____

_____

THESE CHALLENGES I HAVE EXPERIENCED...

_____

_____

_____

_____

_____

_____

I am grateful for...

THIS RISK I TOOK:

_____

_____

_____

_____

THIS SACRIFICE I MADE:

_____

_____

_____

_____

THIS HARD DECISION I MADE:

_____

_____

_____

_____

I am grateful for...

THIS BIG CHANGE THAT HAPPENED IN MY LIFE:

_____

_____

_____

_____

THIS THING ABOUT MYSELF:

_____

_____

_____

_____

THIS TALENT OR SKILL I HAVE:

_____

_____

_____

_____

I am grateful for...

THESE THINGS ABOUT MY GIRLFRIEND...

_____

_____

_____

_____

_____

_____

_____

_____

_____

_____

_____

Questions about me...

MY USUAL COFFEE SHOP ORDER IS...

_____

_____

_____

MY FAVORITE CARD GAME IS...

_____

MY DREAM CAR IS...

_____

MY FAVORITE SEASON OF THE YEAR IS...

_____

MY FAVORITE HOLIDAY IS...

_____

MY GO-TO KARAOKE SONG IS...

_____

_____

IF I COULD LIVE ANYWHERE IN THE WORLD FOR A YEAR WITH ALL
EXPENSES PAID, I WOULD CHOOSE TO LIVE HERE...

_____

_____

MY BIGGEST FEAR IS...

_____

_____

THE SUPERPOWER I WOULD PICK FOR MYSELF IS...

_____

_____

THE MOVIE I HAVE WATCHED THE GREATEST NUMBER OF TIMES IS...

_____

_____

MY LONGEST FRIENDSHIP HAS BEEN WITH...

_____

_____

MY FAVORITE PIZZA TOPPINGS ARE...

_____

_____

MY CURRENT FAVORITE TELEVISION SHOW IS...

_____

_____

IN MY OPINION, THE CORRECT WAY TO HANG A ROLL OF TOILET PAPER IS... (TISSUE OVER THE TOP OR TO THE BACK)

_____

MY FAVORITE THING TO DO IN MY FREE TIME IS...

_____

_____

_____

IF I WOKE UP TOMORROW AND FOUND MYSELF IN CHARGE OF THE COUNTRY, THE FIRST THREE THINGS I WOULD MAKE THE LAW ARE...

1. _____

_____

2. _____

_____

3. _____

_____

MY FAVORITE OUTDOOR ACTIVITY IS...

_____

_____

IF I COULD PICK TO SEE A LIVE SHOW BY ANY MUSICIAN/BAND
WHO HAS EVER EXISTED, I WOULD CHOOSE...

_____

_____

_____

THE LAST BOOK I READ IS...

_____

_____

IF I HAD TO PICK ONE FAVORITE MEMORY OF A TIME I SPENT
WITH MY GIRLFRIEND, I WOULD PICK...

_____

_____

_____

_____

_____

_____

Questions about her (also known as, "guess carefully") ...

HER USUAL COFFEE SHOP ORDER IS...

_____

_____

HER FAVORITE CARD GAME IS...

_____

MY GIRLFRIEND'S DREAM CAR IS...

_____

HER FAVORITE SEASON OF THE YEAR IS...

_____

AND HER FAVORITE HOLIDAY IS...

_____

HER GO-TO KARAOKE SONG IS...

_____

_____

IF SHE COULD LIVE ANYWHERE IN THE WORLD FOR A YEAR WITH ALL EXPENSES PAID, MY GIRLFRIEND WOULD CHOOSE TO LIVE HERE...

_____

_____

HER BIGGEST FEAR IS...

_____

_____

THE SUPERPOWER SHE WOULD PICK FOR HERSELF IS...

_____

_____

THE MOVIE SHE HAS WATCHED THE GREATEST NUMBER OF TIMES IS...

_____

_____

MY GIRLFRIEND'S LONGEST FRIENDSHIP IS WITH...

_____

_____

HER FAVORITE PIZZA TOPPINGS ARE...

_____

_____

MY GIRLFRIEND'S CURRENT FAVORITE TELEVISION SHOW IS...

_____

_____

SHE THINKS THAT THE CORRECT WAY TO HANG A ROLL OF TOILET PAPER IS... (TISSUE OVER THE TOP OR TO THE BACK)

_____

HER FAVORITE THING TO DO IN HER FREE TIME IS...

_____

_____

_____

IF MY GIRLFRIEND WOKE UP TOMORROW AND FOUND HERSELF IN CHARGE OF THE COUNTRY, THE FIRST THREE THINGS SHE WOULD MAKE THE LAW ARE...

1. _____

_____

2. _____

_____

3. _____

_____

HER FAVORITE OUTDOOR ACTIVITY IS...

_____

_____

IF SHE COULD PICK TO SEE A LIVE SHOW BY ANY MUSICIAN/BAND WHO HAS EVER EXISTED, SHE WOULD CHOOSE...

_____

_____

_____

THE LAST BOOK SHE READ IS...

_____

_____

IF SHE WAS TO PICK ONE FAVORITE MEMORY OF A TIME WE TOGETHER, SHE WOULD PICK...

_____

_____

_____

_____

_____

_____

A few of my personal proudest accomplishments are...

1. _____

2. _____

3. _____

4. _____

5. _____

6. _____

7. _____

8. _____

9. _____

10. _____

11. _____

12. _____

13. _____

14. _____

15. _____

And here are a few of things I am proud of my girlfriend for accomplishing...

1. _____

2. _____

3. _____

4. _____

5. _____

6. _____

7. _____

8. _____

9. _____

10. _____

11. _____

12. _____

13. _____

14. _____

15. _____

Sports memories...

WHEN I WAS A KID, I THOUGHT A LOT ABOUT PLAYING THIS
PROFESSIONAL SPORT...

_____

_____

MY FAVORITE PLAYER OF ALL TIME IN ANY SPORT IS...

_____

_____

IF MONEY WAS NO OBJECT, THE SPORTING EVENT I WOULD
WANT TO ATTEND IS...

_____

_____

THE MOST CRUSHING DEFEAT I HAVE EXPERIENCED PLAYING OR
WATCHING A SPORTING EVENT IS...

_____

_____

_____

MY FAVORITE SPORTS MOVIE OF ALL TIME IS...

_____

_____

MY FAVORITE SPORTS TEAMS ARE...

_____

_____

_____

_____

_____

MY FAVORITE SPORTS MEMORY IS...

_____

_____

_____

_____

_____

_____

Sports Pretend Time...

IF I WAS TOLD I COULD SET UP MY OWN SPORTS FRANCHISE, WITH ALL EXPENSES PAID AND IN ANY CITY IN THE WORLD...,

IT WOULD BE IN THIS SPORT...

_____

_____

AND IN THIS CITY...

_____

_____

THE TEAM MASCOT WOULD BE...

_____

_____

THE TEAM COLORS WOULD BE...

_____

_____

IF I WAS ALLOWED TO PICK ANY EXISTING PLAYER IN THIS SPORT TO BE ON MY TEAM, I WOULD PICK...

_____

_____

USE YOUR IMAGINATION AND BEST ARTISTIC SKILLS TO DRAW YOUR TEAM'S LOGO...

My travel stories...

MY LAST BIG VACATION TRIP WAS TO...,

_____

MY THOUGHTS ON FLYING FOR SHORT DISTANCES ARE...

_____

_____

AND FOR LONG DISTANCES...

_____

_____

THE CURRENT STATE OF MY PASSPORT IS (ACTIVE, EXPIRED, NEED TO GET ONE) ...,

_____

LATELY, I HAVE BEEN THINKING THAT IT WOULD GREAT TO TAKE A TRIP TO...

_____

_____

AND THE PLACE I WOULD TRAVEL TO IF TIME AND MONEY WERE NO CONCERN IS...

_____

_____

A FEW OF THE PLACES I HAVE TRAVELED TO ARE...

1. _____

2. _____

3. _____

4. _____

5. _____

6. _____

7. _____

8. _____

9. _____

10. _____

11. _____

12. _____

13. _____

14. _____

15. _____

More questions about me...

MY DREAM JOB IS...

_____

THE ACTOR OR ACTRESS THAT I ABSOLUTELY MUST WATCH
EVERYTHING THEY ARE IN IS...

_____

MY FAVORITE SANDWICH IS...

_____

I LIKE MY EGGS COOKED THIS WAY...

_____

AND MY STEAK COOKED THIS WAY...

_____

THIS IS HOW I IDENTIFY MYSELF POLITICALLY...

_____

MY GO-TO FAST-FOOD FOOD ITEM IS...

_____

THE LAST TELEVISION SHOW I BINGE WATCHED WAS...

_____

More questions about her (How do you think she would answer?) ...

MY GIRLFRIEND'S DREAM JOB IS...

_____

THE ACTOR OR ACTRESS THAT SHE WATCHES EVERYTHING THEY ARE IN IS...

_____

HER FAVORITE SANDWICH IS...

_____

SHE LIKES HER EGGS COOKED THIS WAY...

_____

AND HER STEAK COOKED THIS WAY...

_____

THIS IS HOW SHE IDENTIFIES HERSELF POLITICALLY...

_____

HER GO-TO FAST-FOOD FOOD ITEM IS...

_____

THE LAST TELEVISION SHOW SHE BINGE WATCHED WAS...

_____

_____

More questions about me...

MY GO-TO COCKTAIL IS...

_____

THIS IS WHAT I THINK OF PINEAPPLE ON PIZZA...

_____

MY TOLERANCE FOR SPICY FOOD IS ...

_____

MY FAVORITE DESSERT IS...

_____

MY TYPICAL BREAKFAST IS...

_____

MY FAVORITE SNACK IS...

_____

MY FAVORITE BEVERAGE IS...

_____

THE FOOD ITEMS I ABSOLUTELY REFUSE TO EAT ARE...

_____

_____

_____

More questions about her (How do you think she would answer?) ...

HER GO-TO COCKTAIL IS...

_____

THIS IS WHAT SHE THINKS OF PINEAPPLE ON PIZZA...

_____

HER TOLERANCE FOR SPICY FOOD IS ...

_____

HER FAVORITE DESSERT IS...

_____

HER TYPICAL BREAKFAST IS...

_____

HER FAVORITE SNACK IS...

_____

HER FAVORITE BEVERAGE IS...

_____

THE FOOD ITEMS SHE ABSOLUTELY REFUSES TO EAT ARE...

_____

_____

_____

My top 5 favorite things to eat...

Her top 5 favorite things to eat...

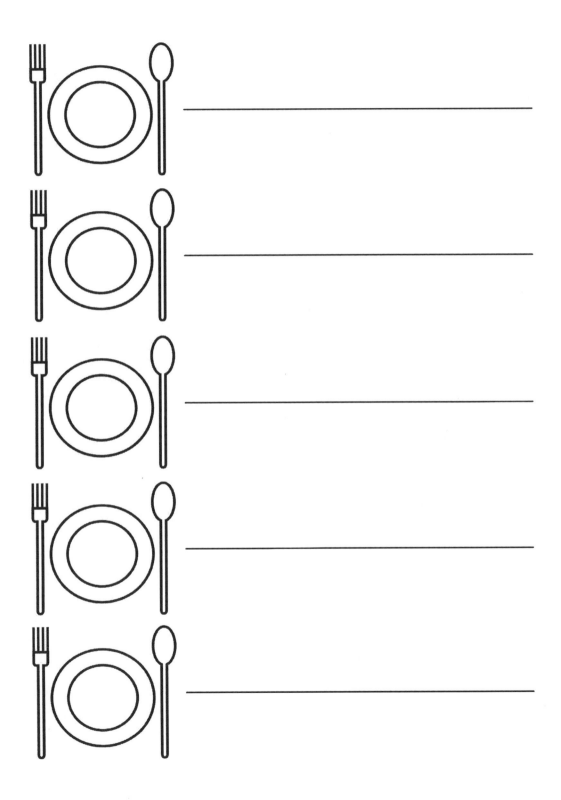

Top 10

THE TEN BOOKS THAT HAVE I LOVE AND/OR MAJORLY IMPACTED
THE WAY I THINK, WORK, OR LIVE MY LIFE ARE...

1. _____

2. _____

3. _____

4. _____

5. _____

6. _____

7. _____

8. _____

9. _____

10. _____

IF I HAD TO PICK TEN OF MY FAVORITE TELEVISION SHOWS OF ALL TIME, I WOULD PICK...

1. _____

2. _____

3. _____

4. _____

5. _____

6. _____

7. _____

8. _____

9. _____

10. _____

IF I HAD TO PICK TEN OF MY FAVORITE MOVIES OF ALL TIME, I WOULD PICK...

1. _____

2. _____

3. _____

4. _____

5. _____

6. _____

7. _____

8. _____

9. _____

10. _____

IF I HAD TO PICK TEN OF MY FAVORITE BANDS OR MUSICIANS OF
ALL TIME, I WOULD PICK...

1. _____

2. _____

3. _____

4. _____

5. _____

6. _____

7. _____

8. _____

9. _____

10. _____

IF I HAD TO PICK TEN OF MY FAVORITE VIDEO GAMES OF ALL TIME, I WOULD PICK...

1. _____

2. _____

3. _____

4. _____

5. _____

6. _____

7. _____

8. _____

9. _____

10. _____

IF I HAD TO PICK TEN OF MY FAVORITE TIMES SPENT WITH MY GIRLFRIEND, I WOULD PICK...

1. _____

2. _____

3. _____

4. _____

5. _____

6. _____

7. _____

8. _____

9. _____

10. _____

Fifteen things I want...

TO DO THIS YEAR...

1. _____

2. _____

3. _____

4. _____

5. _____

6. _____

7. _____

8. _____

9. _____

10. _____

11. _____

12. _____

13. _____

14. _____

15. _____

TO DO OVER THE NEXT TEN YEARS...

1. _____

2. _____

3. _____

4. _____

5. _____

6. _____

7. _____

8. _____

9. _____

10. _____

11. _____

12. _____

13. _____

14. _____

15. _____

SKILLS OR ABILITIES I WANT TO LEARN...

1. _____

2. _____

3. _____

4. _____

5. _____

6. _____

7. _____

8. _____

9. _____

10. _____

11. _____

12. _____

13. _____

14. _____

15. _____

TO TRAVEL TO...

1. _____

2. _____

3. _____

4. _____

5. _____

6. _____

7. _____

8. _____

9. _____

10. _____

11. _____

12. _____

13. _____

14. _____

15. _____

TO EXPERIENCE...

1. _____

2. _____

3. _____

4. _____

5. _____

6. _____

7. _____

8. _____

9. _____

10. _____

11. _____

12. _____

13. _____

14. _____

15. _____

TO ATTEND OR SEE...

1. _____

2. _____

3. _____

4. _____

5. _____

6. _____

7. _____

8. _____

9. _____

10. _____

11. _____

12. _____

13. _____

14. _____

15. _____

OTHER THINGS I ABSOLUTELY NEED TO DO, SEE, LEARN, VISIT, ETC...

1. _____

2. _____

3. _____

4. _____

5. _____

6. _____

7. _____

8. _____

9. _____

10. _____

11. _____

12. _____

13. _____

14. _____

15. _____

16. _____

17. _____

18. _____

19. _____

20. _____

21. _____

22. _____

23. _____

24. _____

25. _____

26. _____

27. _____

28. _____

29. _____

30. _____

Looking forward...

THIS IS WHAT I WANT MY LIFE TO LOOK FIVE YEARS FROM TODAY...

_____

_____

_____

_____

_____

_____

_____

_____

_____

_____

_____

THIS IS WHAT I WANT MY LIFE TO LOOK TWENTY-FIVE YEARS
FROM TODAY...

_____

_____

_____

_____

_____

_____

_____

_____

_____

_____

_____

This is the Ta Dah Page

YEP, YOU'RE DONE.

YOU'VE ANSWERED EVERY QUESTION, COMPLETED ALL THE ACTIVITIES (AT LEAST MOST OF THEM), AND YOU'VE SHARED YOUR MEMORIES AND YOUR THOUGHTS.

YOU'VE HAD SOME FUN AND ALLOWED YOURSELF TO OPEN UP AND TALK ABOUT YOURSELF.

MOST OF ALL, YOU NOW KNOW HOW GREAT IT FEELS WHEN ANOTHER PERSON SAYS, "I WANT TO LEARN MORE ABOUT YOU."

(AND HOW THAT IS ESPECIALLY GREAT WHEN IT IS SOMEONE YOU CARE ABOUT.)

WHAT ARE THE NEXT STEPS?

THE FIRST IS TO SHARE YOUR HANDIWORK WITH THE PERSON WHO GAVE YOU THIS BOOK. LOOK THROUGH IT TOGETHER AND TALK ABOUT YOUR RESPONSES.

ADD MORE DETAILS AND DO SOME STORYTELLING WITH YOUR USUAL FLAIR.

ANOTHER IDEA IS TO GET HER A COPY OF "TO MY GIRLFRIEND, I WANT TO HEAR YOUR LIFE STORY." SHE WILL BE THRILLED AND APPRECIATIVE THAT YOU WANT TO KNOW MORE ABOUT HER AND HER LIFE.

NOW GO REWARD YOURSELF AND DO SOMETHING FUN WITH YOUR GIRLFRIEND. WHO KNOWS WHAT MEMORIES AND MOMENTS YOU WILL COLLECT IN THE PROCESS.

"Don't spend your life looking for someone who understands you. Look for someone who wants to."

– Jeffrey Mason

Hear Your Story Books

AT **HEAR YOUR STORY**, WE HAVE CREATED A LINE OF BOOKS FOCUSED ON GIVING EACH OF US A PLACE TO TELL THE UNIQUE STORY OF WHO WE ARE, WHERE WE HAVE BEEN, AND WHERE WE ARE GOING.

SHARING AND HEARING THE STORIES OF THE PEOPLE IN OUR LIFE CREATES CLOSENESS AND UNDERSTANDING, ULTIMATELY STRENGTHENING OUR BONDS.

Available at Amazon, all bookstores, and at HearYourStory.com

- TO MY GIRLFRIEND, I WANT TO HEAR YOUR STORY

- MOM, I WANT TO HEAR YOUR STORY: A MOTHER'S GUIDED JOURNAL TO SHARE HER LIFE & HER LOVE

- DAD, I WANT TO HEAR YOUR STORY: A FATHER'S GUIDED JOURNAL TO SHARE HIS LIFE & HIS LOVE

- GRANDMOTHER, I WANT TO HEAR YOUR STORY: A GRANDMOTHER'S GUIDED JOURNAL TO SHARE HER LIFE AND HER LOVE

- GRANDFATHER, I WANT TO HEAR YOUR STORY: A GRANDFATHER'S GUIDED JOURNAL TO SHARE HIS LIFE AND HIS LOVE

- TELL YOUR LIFE STORY: THE WRITE YOUR OWN AUTOBIOGRAPHY GUIDED JOURNAL

Hear Your Story
Books

- TO MY WONDERFUL AUNT, I WANT TO HEAR YOUR STORY: A GUIDED JOURNAL TO SHARE HER LIFE AND HER LOVE

- TO MY UNCLE, I WANT TO HEAR YOUR STORY: A GUIDED JOURNAL TO SHARE HIS LIFE AND HIS LOVE

- LIFE GAVE ME YOU; I WANT TO HEAR YOUR STORY: A GUIDED JOURNAL FOR STEPMOTHERS TO SHARE THEIR LIFE STORY

- YOU CHOOSE TO BE MY DAD; I WANT TO HEAR YOUR STORY: A GUIDED JOURNAL FOR STEPDADS TO SHARE THEIR LIFE STORY

- LOVE NOTES: I WROTE THIS BOOK ABOUT YOU

- GETTING TO KNOW YOU: 201 FUN QUESTIONS TO DEEPEN YOUR RELATIONSHIP AND HEAR EACH OTHER'S STORY

- YOU, ME, AND US: 229 FUN RELATIONSHIP QUESTIONS TO ASK YOUR GUY OR GIRL

- BECAUSE I LOVE YOU: THE COUPLE'S BUCKET LIST THAT BUILDS YOUR RELATIONSHIP

- THE STORY OF EXPECTING YOU: A SELFCARE PREGNANCY GUIDED JOURNAL AND MEMORY BOOK

About the Author

JEFFREY MASON WAS RAISED IN A SMALL TOWN IN TEXAS BEFORE LEAVING TO SERVE AS A HOSPITAL CORPSMAN WITH THE UNITED STATES NAVY AND UNITED STATES MARINE CORPS. AFTER HIS MILITARY SERVICE, HE STUDIED AT CHABOT COMMUNITY COLLEGE AND AT CALIFORNIA STATE UNIVERSITY, SACRAMENTO.

TO DATE, JEFFREY HAS WRITTEN 23 BOOKS, MOSTLY CENTERED AROUND THE DISCOVERY, AND SHARING OF PERSONAL AND FAMILY HISTORIES. THIS MISSION INSPIRED HIM TO CREATE **HEAR YOUR STORY**, A COMPANY WITH THE MISSION TO MAKE IT SIMPLE FOR ANYONE TO REMINISCE AND SHARE THE STORIES OF THEIR LIFE, WHILE ALSO CREATING CHERISHED MEMORIES THAT CAN BE PASSED FROM GENERATION TO GENERATION.

FOR EVERY BOOK SOLD, **HEAR YOUR STORY** DONATES A PERCENTAGE OF ITS PROFITS TO A NON-PROFIT ORGANIZATION. TO DATE, THESE CONTRIBUTIONS HAVE BENEFITTED ALZHEIMER'S RESEARCH AND CARE, DOMESTIC VIOLENCE PREVENTION, AND HELPING KIDS MANAGE DEPRESSION AND SOCIAL ANXIETY.

YOU CAN CONTACT JEFFREY DIRECTLY AT HELLO@JEFFREYMASON.COM, AT HTTPS://HEARYOURSTORY.COM, OR AT HTTPS://WWW.JEFFREYMASON.COM.

HE WOULD BE GRATEFUL IF YOU WOULD HELP PEOPLE FIND HIS BOOKS BY LEAVING A REVIEW ON AMAZON. YOUR FEEDBACK HELPS HIM GET BETTER AT THIS THING HE LOVES.

Made in the USA
Middletown, DE
07 February 2023

24140322R00075